The figure shown is a model

AVOIDING
DANGER FROM
UNDERGROUND
SERVICES

HSG47

HSE BOOKS

© Crown copyright 2000

Applications for reproduction should be made in writing to:
Copyright Unit, Her Majesty's Stationery Office,
St Clements House, 2-16 Colegate, Norwich NR3 1BQ

First published 2000

ISBN 0 7176 1744 0

This guidance is issued by the Health and Safety Executive. Following the
guidance is not compulsory and you are free to take other action. But if you
do follow the guidance you will normally be doing enough to comply with
the law. Health and safety inspectors seek to secure compliance with the law
and may refer to this guidance as illustrating good practice.

CONTENTS

INTRODUCTION

1   This book updates the guidance contained in the previous edition of HSG47 *Avoiding danger from underground services*. It outlines the dangers which can arise from work near underground services and gives advice on how to reduce the risk. It deals only with risks to the health and safety of people and is not concerned with damage which has no direct risks associated with it. However, precautions taken which reduce risks to the health and safety of people will generally also reduce the risk of damage to services. Remember too that damage can have a knock-on effect: consider for example the effect of the loss of a telephone service if a 999 call has to be made.

Where this guidance applies

2   This guidance applies to situations where underground services may be found and where **work involves penetrating the ground at or below surface level.** Buried services are widespread and it should be assumed they are present unless it has been shown otherwise.

3   However, for road resurfacing where ground penetration is contained within the wearing and base courses, the services encountered are likely to be limited to traffic sensor cables. Care will still need to be taken, in particular to avoid damage to surface boxes for valves, pressure points, test points etc. All other work will be covered by this guidance including work in footways and kerbing, regardless of depth, as underground services may be found very near the surface.

Who this guidance is aimed at

4   This guidance is aimed primarily at clients, designers, planning supervisors, contractors, employers, owners and operators of underground services, managers and supervisors and others concerned with planning, organising and supervising work near such services. This includes work by or for the utilities and also roadworks, construction and demolition work. However, it is relevant to anyone who has responsibilities under relevant legislation (see Appendix 1) and contains a suggested text for use by employees who work near underground services (see Appendix 2).

How to use this guidance

5   Guidance on the general precautions to be taken to prevent damage to all types of underground services is contained in the section 'Safe systems of work'. Additional guidance for each type of buried service is given in the section 'Precautions for particular services', which should be read in conjunction with 'Safe systems of work'.

Definitions

6   The term 'service(s)' means all underground pipes, cables and equipment associated with the electricity, gas, water (including piped sewage) and telecommunications industries. It also

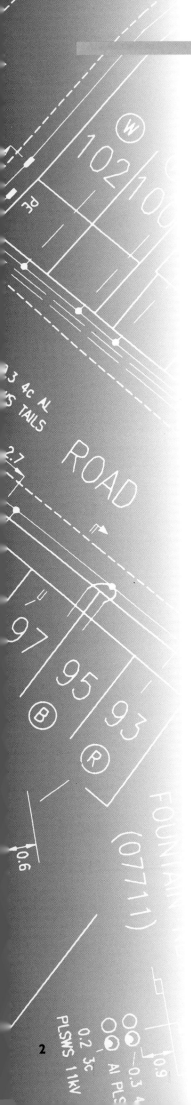

includes other pipelines which transport a range of petrochemical and other fluids. It does not include underground structures such as railway tunnels etc.

7　　The term 'service connection(s)' means pipes or cables between distribution mains and individual premises.

THE DANGERS

8　　Damage to underground services can cause fatal or severe injury. The main dangers are outlined in paragraphs 9 to 18.

Electricity cables

9　　Injuries are usually caused by the explosive effects of arcing current, and by any associated fire or flames which may result, when a live cable is penetrated by a sharp object such as the point of a tool (see front cover). Such effects can also occur when a cable is crushed severely enough to cause internal contact between the conductors or between metallic sheathing and one or more conductors. Injuries are typically severe, potentially fatal, burns to the hands, face and body. Direct electric shock is less likely.

10　Incidents may also arise from cables which have been damaged but left unreported and unrepaired.

11　Other nearby services, such as plastic gas pipes, may also be at risk from damaged live electricity cables. This could result in explosions and a greater fire risk.

Gas pipes

12　Damage to gas pipes can cause leaks which may lead to fire or explosion (see Figure 1). There are two types of damage:

■　that which causes an immediate leak;

■　that which causes a leak some time later. The damage may occur at the time the work is carried out or subsequently: for example poor reinstatement may leave a pipe inadequately supported or subject to unequal forces.

Figure 1 Aftermath of a gas explosion, following damage to an underground gas service pipe

Water pipes and sewers

13 Although damage to water pipes is less likely to result in injury, the following may occur:

■ a jet of water from a main can injure a person. It may also contain stones or other hard objects ejected from the ground around the pipe;

■ leaks of water from underground pipes can affect adjacent services and reduce support for other structures, for example:
  ● damage to mains can result in flooding, leading to subsequent risks from drowning or the rapid collapse of support to the sides of an excavation;
  ● water can enter gas pipes if they are also damaged.

14 While some sewage is pumped at pressure, sewers are generally gravity-fed, and the main hazard from damage to a sewer is the possibility of contamination.

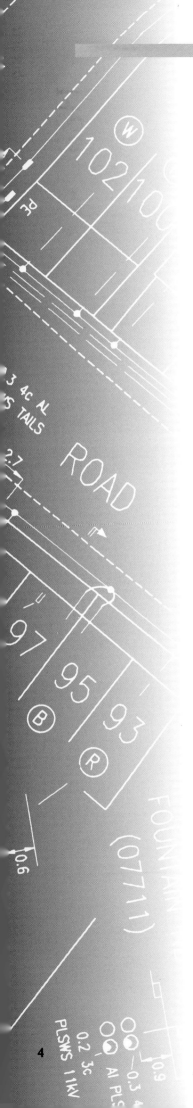

Other pipelines

15 The danger arising from damage to other pipelines depends on the nature of the conveyed fluid. Fluids and their associated dangers include:

- flammable liquids and gases - risk of fire and explosion;

- all fluids at elevated pressure - risk of injury from sudden release of contents;

- toxic liquids and gases - risk of poisoning; and

- gases such as nitrogen, argon etc - risk of asphyxiation.

16 Very often a fluid will present a combination of risks, for example a liquid may be both toxic and flammable.

Telecommunication cables

17 Damage to telecommunication and cable TV cables may require expensive repairs and can cause considerable disruption to those relying on the system. However, the risks of direct personal injury are normally very low.

18 Flammable and toxic gases can enter cable-carrying ducts, particularly if the duct has been damaged. Such gases can accumulate in chambers, manholes etc and pose a risk to operatives who may need to work there.

SAFE SYSTEMS OF WORK

General

19 A safe system of work has four basic elements:

- planning the work;

- plans;

- cable- and pipe-locating devices;

- safe digging practices.

20 These key elements complement each other, and **all four** should be used when working near buried services. More details of each are given in the sections that follow. A flow diagram, describing part of the process, is on page 5.

Figure 2   Flow diagram

This flow diagram is intended to help give an understanding of the process **from referring to plans on site through to the start of excavation**, for example when excavating in a road or footway. However it:

■   describes *only part* of the process; it does not, for example, describe planning the work, including reference to plans at the design stage;

■   is a simplified picture and not a substitute for reading the text;

■   is not a substitute for a suitable and sufficient risk assessment;

■   does not take account of a number of other situations, eg cables embedded in concrete or those situations where resiting services is proposed.

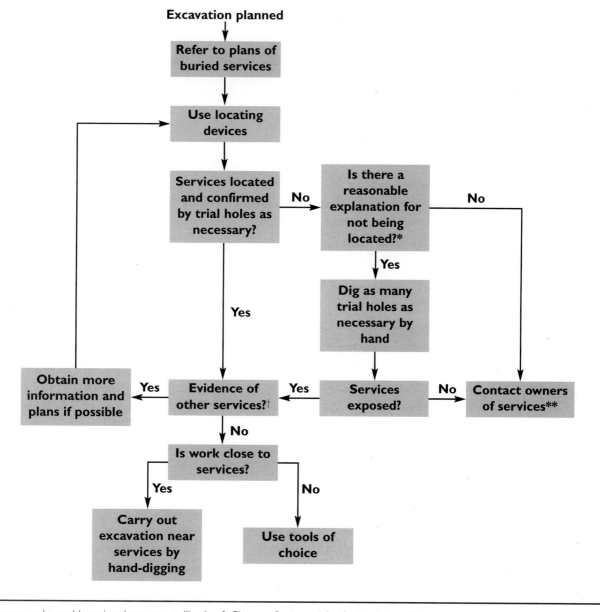

* For example, could services be non-metallic pipes? Please refer to text for further information.
† In particular, visual evidence. Ensure that the presence of services, which may be unmarked on plans or for which no plans are available, has been considered, for example service connections.
** If there is visual evidence of services, but owners cannot be traced, despite all reasonable attempts to do so, any excavation could proceed but using hand-dug trial holes and proceeding with great care.

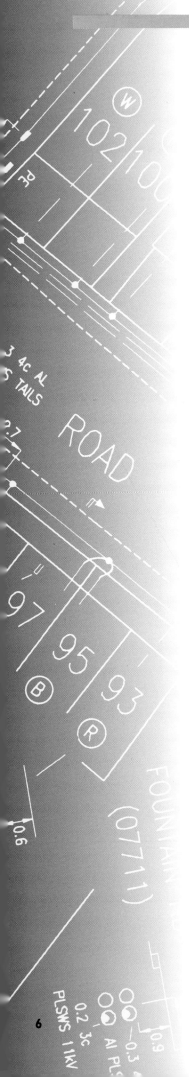

21 People responsible for planning or carrying out relevant work should liaise with the service owners/operators. It is important that owners/operators accept the need for close co-operation with those who have to excavate in the vicinity of their services. They should be prepared to help locate and identify the services when asked to do so, perhaps by sending a representative to the site. They should also consider further ways of improving and extending co-operation, particularly with other utilities, local authorities and contractors who have to perform a considerable amount of road and footway excavation.

22 When carrying out excavations, it is also important to:

■ use the appropriate traffic signing on highways; this is described in a Code of Practice *Safety at street works and road works;*[1]

■ avoid risks from other sources. Further information can be found in HSG185 *Health and safety in excavations.*[2]

Training and supervision

23 Employees should receive adequate instruction and training in correct procedures and the precautions to be taken. Appendix 2 could be used as a basis for training programmes. The Construction Industry Training Board (CITB)[*] can also give advice on available training. Note also that under the New Roads and Street Works Act 1991, a supervisor and at least one on-site operative at street works should have prescribed qualifications (see Appendix 1, paragraph 24).

24 Supervision should reflect the risks involved. Given the peripatetic nature of the work, the hazards involved and - as excavation proceeds - the changing nature of those hazards and conditions, supervisors should check regularly that, among other things, the work is being carried out according to instructions and that all precautions necessary are in place.

Planning the work

25 Many dangers can be avoided by careful planning before the work starts. Risk assessments should consider how the work is to be carried out, ensuring local circumstances are taken into account.

26 A permit system may be appropriate for particularly hazardous work. This would involve written authorisation by a responsible person, identifying the work to be done and the precautions to be taken. A permit system needs suitable supervision and monitoring to ensure that the conditions of a permit are complied with.

---

* Construction Industry Training Board, Bircham Newton, King's Lynn, Norfolk PE31 6RH
Tel: 01485 577577.

27   The Construction (Design and Management) Regulations 1994 (CDM) provide a framework for the management of risks. The Regulations apply to demolition, notifiable projects and those involving more than four people, except that the designer's duties under regulation 13 will always apply. Guidance for designers is given in the 'Design' section (see paragraphs 30 to 40). Further information on the application of the Regulations can be found in L54 *Managing construction for health and safety* and *A guide to managing health and safety in construction*.[3,4]

28   Even where the CDM Regulations do not apply in full, risks remain. The advice under 'Where CDM applies' (paragraphs 41 to 48) should help clients, contractors and others to comply with their duties towards employees, contractors and the public under the Health and Safety at Work etc Act 1974 (HSW Act) and under other health and safety legislation (see Appendix 1).

29   Further information on risk assessment and the management of health and safety can also be found in *Management of health and safety at work*.[5]

Design

30   The term 'design' includes drawings, design details, specifications, and bills of quantities. A designer is anyone who prepares these. For example, people planning the route of a new cable television scheme are designers. Designers will need to know if there are buried services present.

31   For building work, resiting the services away from the work is most often a reasonably practicable means of avoiding the risk. The service owner/operator should be asked to do this. Such requests will need to include a sufficient period of notice.

32   Other options to resiting the services may include:

■   repositioning structures or parts of structures to ensure that services are avoided during the work;

■   arranging for the supply to be disconnected during the work;*

■   if none of these are possible, choosing methods to avoid the services, for example by using ground beams.

33   Permanent structures such as buildings should generally not be built over the services, as this may introduce additional risks to construction workers and can prevent future access to the services. If it is not possible to avoid building structures over any service, arrangements should be made with the utility to relocate the services in a duct, or something similar.

---

* For periods of notice required by legislation to disconnect a service to a customer, contact the relevant utility or respective regulator. For example, for the periods of notice for electricity (paragraph 103 gives those current at the time of publication) contact Ofgem, Hagley House, Hagley Road, Edgbaston, Birmingham B16 8QG, who publish details of these and other performance standards annually in their *Report on customer services*.

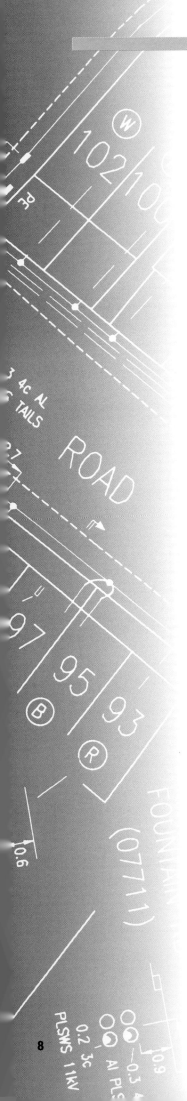

34 Designers should not overlook ancillary work including the erection of perimeter fencing and walling, or the position of roadways onto the site which may affect services at the site perimeter. Early identification and planning are essential if risks are to be controlled during the construction phase of the project.

35 Where new services such as electrical or gas supplies are being installed, it may be possible sometimes to reduce risks by not installing or commissioning them until other groundworks and work on the installation have been completed.

36 The options facing designers planning a new service in a roadway may be more limited. It is important to have information about existing services to help select a route for the new service which avoids them. The risk of contact with existing services can be reduced by choosing a route with a low density of buried services. For example, a cable television duct might be routed at the side of a road if there is a reduced cable density there. Designers of pipelines should also be aware of the guidance contained in the HSE publication *A guide to the Pipelines Safety Regulations 1996*[6] which advises that the parallel running of similar pipelines in the street should be avoided. Liaison with the owners of services is important as they are in a position to provide information to the designers to enable such decisions to be made.

37 Having reduced the risks to a level as low as reasonably practicable by design, information should be provided by the designer(s) about the risks which remain. In most cases the best way of informing contractors and individuals doing the work is by providing the information on drawings, ensuring that the information is the best available. When excavations are undertaken in the vicinity of buried services it is very important that operatives have access to clear, readable and accurate plans showing the location of buried services.

38 Among their other duties to provide information, designers are specifically required to make the client aware of when project work falls within the scope of the CDM Regulations.

39 Further information for designers can be found in *Designing for health and safety in construction.*[7]

40 Designers are likely to find other information in the rest of this document useful, but note in particular the sections on 'Plans', and 'Some specific sites and situations'.

Where CDM applies

41   This section describes procedures that should be followed in addition to the designers' duties, as a result of the CDM Regulations applying in full.

42   A client is a person or organisation for whom a project is carried out. In general, where a utility company is asked to provide permanent services for a building development, the utility will be acting as a contractor, and will be required to act under the direction of the principal contractor while on site.

43   However, where the provision of services can be physically separated and demarcated from the site, then the utility will usually be acting as a client for the purposes of CDM. If the utility undertakes the work itself, then it will usually be a client and contractor. Where the work is undertaken by others, then they will be contractors in the usual way for the purposes of CDM.

44   Clients have a duty to make reasonable enquiries about buried services, and pass relevant information to the planning supervisor, who should include it in the pre-tender health and safety plan. Information on buried services may be available from the client's own health and safety file. If it is, remember that it may have been obtained for previous work and may be out of date. Up-to-date information should be included in the pre-tender health and safety plan (and ultimately transferred to the file).

45   Tenderers should outline how they intend to manage the risks from buried services, also indicating the resources to be provided.

46   Contractors arriving on site should be provided with information about the risks from buried services (see Figure 3). The principal contractor may make site rules (for example specifying acceptable types of equipment; the safe digging practices which may be used on site; working procedures; and commissioning procedures). Where services have been disconnected, this should be recorded and issued to the contractors working in that area. Contractors should co-operate with the principal contractor to ensure that any rules or agreed methods of working are adhered to.

47   The planning supervisor should ensure that the health and safety file contains updated information on buried services, for the benefit of those carrying out subsequent work. Whether the project involves excavating in the roadway to install a new service or to repair or maintain an existing service, a file will still be required where CDM applies.

48   If the client is a utility, the file information should allow them to update their own records on the position of their services and should be made available to others who will need to use this information for subsequent maintenance, repair and construction work.

Figure 3 Discussing the work on site

Plans

Obtaining information on services

49 Plans or other suitable information about all buried services in the area should be obtained before excavation work starts, when the work is being planned. Most buried services belong to one of the utilities. Those that do not are likely to be found on or near commercial, industrial, military or other sites. Wherever possible owners/operators should be consulted. It should be remembered that for a number of types of service there may be more than one owner/operator in an area.

50 The use of 'one-call' systems is recommended where available.* This allows those who wish to excavate, and who give sufficient notice, to obtain plans from a range of owners and operators through one contact. In addition, because of the difficulty in detecting some telecommunication cables and the cost of damage to them, telecommunication companies may prefer to visit the site to locate the cables.†

---

* At the time of publication, a 'one-call' system is available in Cheshire for pipelines and in Scotland for all services where the excavation is not on behalf of the utilities. Telephone Susiephone 'Dial before you dig' Freephone: 0800 800333.
† Contact the telecommunication company for further details. The system may also be referred to as a 'Dial-before-you-dig' system.

51 Where it is not possible for those undertaking the excavation work to obtain information, as may be the case when emergency* work has to be undertaken, the work should be carried out as though there are buried services in the area.

52 Account should be taken of any indications that buried services exist, such as the presence of lamp-posts, illuminated traffic signs, gas service pipes entering buildings, pit covers, pipeline marker posts, evidence of reinstated trenches etc. However, if there are no such indications, this does not mean that there are no buried services.

Provision of plans by service owners

53 Owners/operators should provide either up-to-date, readable plans, which show the recorded line and depth (where known) of all their known services buried in the proposed work area, or other suitable information which achieves the same aim. A symbol key is likely to be important to help the recipient understand the plans.

54 Owners/operators should do everything reasonably practicable to ensure that such information is made available to enquirers. They are likely to receive many routine applications for information and should consider how best to make information available at short notice. Where reasonably practicable, arrangements should also be made to deal with emergencies outside office hours so that operatives can be given plans of underground services when they receive their work instructions. Some owners/operators may have reservations, for reasons of security, about supplying copies of their underground services plans for areas such as those around important civil and military establishments. In such cases an alternative method should be used; for example a representative could be sent to the site to give information to legitimate contractors/utilities etc.

55 Utilities have made agreements to exchange records, as described in *Recommendations for the exchange of records of apparatus between utilities*.[8]

Use and limitation of plans

56 Plans vary in scale, content and style. Two examples are shown on pages 23 and 29. Adequate instruction and training in how to read and interpret plans should be given to anyone who needs to use them.

57 Plans can give an indication of the location, configuration and number of underground services at a particular site, and should help subsequent tracing by locating devices. However, they are rarely drawn accurately to scale and, even if they claim to be, they should not be relied upon to obtain distances. For example, errors may have been made during drafting, or reproduction may have changed the scale, especially if the plan was

---

* The New Roads and Street Works Act 1991 defines emergency works in relation to circumstances which are likely to cause danger to people or property. If the question arises in criminal or civil proceedings whether or not works were emergency works, it is for the person alleging that they were to prove that this was the case. Clients and contractors should not use 'emergency work' as an excuse to justify a failure to plan properly when starting work without plans or other suitable information about buried services in the area.

obtained from a microfiche slide or digital map. Accuracy may be further limited because:

- the position of reference points (eg the kerb line) may have changed since the plans were drawn;

- regrading of the surface may mean that the depths shown are now incorrect;

- services, particularly cables, may have been moved without the knowledge of their owners/operators;

- in many cases service connections are not marked;

- services, marked as straight lines may, in practice, snake. Excessively long cables may have been laid in horizontal loops outside substations, switch rooms etc;

- plans may show spare ducts; and

- the routes of older services in particular may not have been recorded, so the absence of records should never be taken as proof that the area in question is free of underground services.

58   These limitations make it very important that other indicators (for examples see paragraph 52) are taken into account and that suitable locating devices and safe digging methods are used. Further notes on the use and limitations of plans for electricity cables and gas pipes are given in 'Precautions for particular services'.

59   In certain cases, such as construction site work and large-scale road excavation work, it is recommended to transfer the information onto the working plans for the guidance of those carrying out the work. Information transferred should include all relevant features, such as valve pits, depths etc. Particular care should be taken where topographical changes have occurred since services were laid.

Cable- and pipe-locating devices

60   The position of any services in or near the proposed work area should be pinpointed as accurately as possible by means of a locating device (see Figure 4), using plans, and other information (see paragraph 52) as a guide to the possible location of services and to help interpret the signal.

Types of locating devices

61   The main types available can be classed
     as follows:

■   *Hum detectors* are receiving instruments
     which detect the magnetic field radiated
     by electricity cables which have a current
     flowing through them. They do not
     respond to:
     ● cables where there is little or no
       current flowing, for example
       service connection cables to
       unoccupied premises or street
       lighting cables in the daytime;
     ● direct current cables;
     ● some well-balanced high-voltage
       cables, where these generate
       relatively little field (which in turn
       may be further screened by the
       cable sheathing).

■   *Radio frequency detectors* are receiving
     instruments which respond to low-
     frequency radio signals, which may be
     picked up and re-emitted by long metallic

Figure 4   Using a cable locator

pipes and cables. If radio frequency detection is used, other metallic objects may re-radiate the
signal and results may vary appreciably according to locality, length of the buried cable or pipe
and distance from the termination and geographical orientation.

■   *Transmitter-receiver instruments* - a small portable transmitter or signal generator can be
     connected to a cable or pipe or placed very close to it so that the signal is introduced into
     it. The receiver can then detect this signal. Usually the location of some part of the cable or
     pipe needs to be already known so that the transmitter can be properly positioned and
     these locators generally require more skill to operate than most other types. They can,
     however, provide useful information in difficult situations where the techniques using hum
     detectors and radio frequency detectors have not been successful.

■   *Metal detectors* - conventional detectors will usually locate flat metal covers, joint boxes etc,
     but may well miss round cables or pipes.

■   *Ground probing radar* - a relatively new method which is capable of detecting anomalies in
     the ground. When these anomalies can be plotted into a continuous line, this may indicate a
     cable, duct or pipe. However, this technique alone would not determine the precise nature
     of the service and it should be supported by information available about the services
     present, and also preferably with the use of other, more conventional, forms of locating

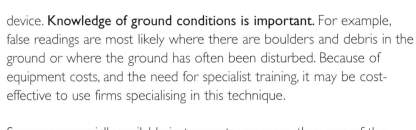

device. **Knowledge of ground conditions is important.** For example, false readings are most likely where there are boulders and debris in the ground or where the ground has often been disturbed. Because of equipment costs, and the need for specialist training, it may be cost-effective to use firms specialising in this technique.

62   Some commercially available instruments use more than one of the techniques listed in paragraph 61 and may include a depth-measuring facility.

Use of locating devices

63   The degree of confidence with which buried services can be detected depends on a number of factors such as:

■   the training, skill, hearing and experience of the operator;

■   the characteristics of the device being used;

■   the calibration and reliability of the locating device;

■   the type, length and depth of the service;

■   for cables, the magnitude of the current being carried; and

■   the effects of other nearby services.

64   It is very important that anyone who uses a locator should have received thorough training in its use and limitations. Locating devices should always be used in accordance with the manufacturer's instructions and should be regularly checked and maintained in good working order.

65   A locator may not be able to distinguish between cables or pipes running close together and may represent them as a single signal. If, for example, two are sited one above the other, the lower one may not be detected. Exposing one cable or pipe does not mean that there is not another close by. **Frequent and repeated use should be made of locators during the course of the work.** Service location is likely to become more accurate as cover is removed.

66   Locators (with the possible exception of ground-probing radar) do not detect plastic pipes or other non-metallic services unless either:

■   a metallic tracer wire has been laid with the pipe. This enables a signal transmitter/receiver to be used. Plastic gas and water pipes are the non-metallic services most likely to be encountered and few have been laid with metallic tracer wires in the past, with the exception of plastic pipes on liquefied petroleum gas (LPG) metered estates; or

■   a small signal transmitter is inserted into and pushed along the pipe. This is a sophisticated technique which is not likely to be appropriate for most jobs.

67   Many telecommunication and railway signalling cables also cannot be located by locating devices, unless metal components (such as a metal sheath) are connected to earth.

68   The line of any identified services should be noted and marked with waterproof crayon, chalk or paint on paved surfaces (use biodegradable paint or erase residual markings as far as possible after excavation), or with wooden pegs in grassed or unsurfaced areas. Steel pins, spikes or long pegs which could damage services laid at shallow depth should not be used.

Safe digging practice

Exposing services

69   Excavation work should be carried out carefully and follow recognised safe digging practices. Once a locating device has been used to determine position and route, excavation may proceed, with trial holes dug using suitable hand tools as necessary to confirm the position of any buried services. Special care should be taken when digging above or close to the assumed line of such a service. **Hand-held power tools and mechanical excavators are the main causes of danger and they should not be used too close to underground services.** Advice on appropriate safety margins from electricity cables, gas pipes and other pipelines is given in the relevant sections of 'Precautions for particular services'.

70   Hand tools can also be a common source of accidents if incorrectly used. However, when used carefully, they can normally provide a satisfactory way of exposing buried services, once the approximate positions have been determined using plans and locators.

71   Every effort should be made to excavate alongside the service rather than directly above it. Final exposure of the service by horizontal digging is recommended, as the force applied to hand tools can be controlled more effectively. In particular:

■   spades and shovels (preferably those with curved edges) should be used rather than other tools. They should not be thrown or spiked into the ground, but eased in with gentle foot pressure;

■   picks, pins or forks may be used with care to free lumps of stone etc, and to break up hard layers of chalk or sandstone;

■   picks should not be used in soft clay or other soft soils near to buried services.

72 Particular care is also necessary:

■ when driving in fence pins or penetrating the ground with any other such object;

■ when gas leak search techniques such as barholing are used.[9] (Normally the gas emergency service would undertake this technique - see paragraph 140.)

73 A proprietary air digging tool, which removes soil with a high-velocity jet of air, can be used to expose buried services without damage to the service (see Figure 5). However, it will not penetrate asphalt, concrete or frozen ground. The precautions needed to prevent injury from ejected soil and other material should be assessed.

74 Once exposed, services may need to be supported and **should never be used as hand- or footholds for climbing out of excavations.**

75 All services should be assumed to be live until disconnected and proven

Figure 5 Using an air digging tool

safe at the point of work. Obtain written confirmation of disconnection from the owner/operator before removing a redundant service.

76 If a buried service suffers damage during the excavation or subsequent work, the owner/operator should be informed. In the case of electricity cables, gas pipes, other pipelines or high-pressure water mains, arrangements should be made to keep people well clear of the area until it has been repaired or otherwise made safe by the owner/operator.

77 Further advice when exposing particular types of services can be found in 'Precautions for particular services'.

Personal protective clothing

78 Burns are the main injuries that result from damage to live buried electrical cables or from fire or explosion following a gas leak. In many cases burns are made more severe by the injured person working bare-chested. Even ordinary work clothing can greatly reduce the severity of the burns and protective clothing is better (for further advice on clothing for work near electricity cables see paragraph 120). However clothing made from man-made fibres such as nylon may melt and stick to the skin, increasing the severity of the burns. The wearing of protective clothing should never be a substitute for a safe system of work.

Identifying exposed services

79 Once underground services have been uncovered, failure to identify them correctly is another common cause of accidents. A wide variety of materials and colours have been used for services over the years. Furthermore some services may be very similar in appearance and some services run in ducts, making them difficult to identify. The following approaches should be adopted until the identity of the service has been positively confirmed:

■ water pipes, electricity cables and telecommunication cables may be covered in black plastic. If any black plastic service is found, it should be assumed to be a live electricity cable;

■ iron and steel water pipes and gas pipelines may appear very similar. If any such pipe is uncovered, it should be treated as if it were a gas pipe;

■ continuously welded steel pipes should always be treated as containing a hazardous or high-pressure fluid;

■ at collieries, beware of electricity cables, some of which are yellow or blue and may be mistaken for other services;

■ on some building sites beware of electricity cables being placed in yellow service pipes or blue water pipes;

■ **where there is any doubt about the identity of an exposed service it should be treated as an electricity cable or gas pipe until proved otherwise.**

80　For modern installations, a national colour coding system for buried services has been agreed by most utilities, as described in the NJUG publication *The identification of small buried mains and services*.[10] In summary, the system is as follows:

Colour	Service
Black	Electricity
Red	Electricity - some high-voltage cables
Orange	Street lighting in England and Wales and traffic control cables
Purple	Road lighting in Scotland
Blue	Water
Yellow	Gas
Grey or white	Telecommunications
Green	Cable television and some telecommunications

81　It is important to remember that:

■　old, non-utility services or other pipelines may not conform to this system;

■　colours may look different under poor or artificial lighting; and

■　ducts could include any of the services, although this is less likely to occur for telecommunication and cable television ducts.

82　This colour coding system should not be confused with the one contained in BS 1710[11] which generally applies to above-ground building and process services.

Backfilling

83　Backfilling of any excavation should be done carefully. Where possible, any warning tiles, tape etc above the services should be put back in their original position unless visual examination after exposure showed this to be incorrect, in which case they should be replaced above the service to which they refer. Warning tape should not be used for any other purpose (for example guarding an excavation) and should not be discarded in an excavation during backfilling. Backfill materials containing items likely to damage the services, such as large pieces of rock and hard core, should not be used. Further information on backfilling can be obtained from:

- utilities and owner/operators, for their particular services;

- paragraph 143 for backfilling around gas pipes (where long-term damage is a particular hazard);

- the Code of Practice (under the New Roads and Street Works Act 1991) *Specification for the reinstatement of openings in highways.*[12]

84   If the plans or other information have proved to be inaccurate (for example a service has been found well away from its recorded position), the owners/operators should be informed (preferably before the excavation is backfilled) and they should amend their records accordingly.

Some specific sites and situations

Safe systems of work for trenchless methods

85   Trenchless methods are increasingly being used for laying and renovating buried pipes and cables, particularly where there is a need to avoid surface disruptions.[13] The most widely used techniques are directional drilling (see Figure 6), impact moling, microtunnelling, pipe bursting and auger boring.

86   Plans, locating devices and trial excavations should be used to locate existing services in the same way as for open cut excavation methods. The route of the device being used should then be planned accordingly. Care should be taken when using trenchless methods to avoid colliding with, and thereby damaging, other services. In addition, if moling or pipe bursting are undertaken too near to other services or ducts, displaced soil may damage or enter them.

87   As a general guide, to avoid damage and to allow sufficient clearance for maintenance of the services, the minimum clearance between adjacent services should be either 250 mm or one and a half times the diameter of the pipe being laid, whichever is the greater. For electricity cables, clearances for maintenance work should be approximately 300 mm.[15] However, clearances for any technique may need to be varied, taking into account such factors as the construction of adjacent plant, ground conditions, bore diameter, the accuracy and reliability of the technique/equipment being used and whether the other plant is parallel to or crosses the proposed line. Any requirements of the owners of adjacent services should be taken into account.

88   Moles are prone to deflection from their original course and if there are existing services in the vicinity a mole tracking device should be used. Where trenchless techniques are used, all equipment should be effectively earthed at all times it is in use, using an equipotential mat as required, in case it hits a power cable causing the machinery to become live.

Figure 6 Horizontal drilling being used for laying a cable under a road

89 Further information can be obtained from *Horizontal directional drilling and impact moling.*[14]

New housing developments

90 Underground services within the confines of partly completed housing developments are especially prone to damage from ongoing construction work. Each utility should keep to its agreed position as in NJUG publication Number 7.[15] A common trench may help to control the position and separation of underground services. Special arrangements may be necessary to restrict vehicle and mobile plant crossings to locations where temporary protection for the services has been provided. Advice on the installation and protection of buried electricity cables feeding plant used for construction work (eg cranes, hoists etc) is given in HSG141 *Electrical safety on construction sites.*[16]

91 Close liaison should be maintained between the developers, their contractors, and the utilities. A marked-up plan of the estate showing the up-to-date position of buried services (including any variations from planned routes) should be kept on site by the builder/developer for the information of those involved in excavation and groundwork.

Installation of new services near existing services

92 New underground services often have to be laid in ground which contains existing services. Where it is reasonably practicable to do so, the utility planning the new installation should aim to site it so that it is separated from all existing buried services by the distances specified in NJUG publication Number 7[15] (some of which are referred to in paragraph 87).

93 Where, because of buried services congestion, this standard cannot be attained, there should be as great a separation as is reasonably practicable. Where the installation of a service would obstruct access to an existing service for more than a few metres, then all reasonably practicable means should be used to avoid this. In particular, the practice of laying multiple ducts directly above other services should be avoided.

94 If the utility or its contractors laying the new service have had to reduce the separation, they should inform the utility whose service has been affected. The utility can then amend their records for future reference.

Demolition sites

95 Special problems can arise in the case of service terminations in derelict property or on demolition sites. Anyone concerned with demolition work should give adequate notice to the relevant gas, electricity and water undertakings of their intention to demolish any premises. Work should not start until either they have confirmed in writing that the supply has been disconnected, or other appropriate safeguarding action has been taken.

96 Buried services on industrial or commercial sites may be owned by the site occupier. A contractor who is to demolish buildings or plant on such a site should contact the owner or occupier, in addition to the utilities and other service operators, to ensure that all relevant services are isolated before work starts.

97 Even where supplies have been disconnected, beware of, for example:

■ services that run through sites and are not part of the site supplies;

■ pot-ended or bottle-ended cables (see paragraph 110); and

  if in doubt, treat services as 'live'.

98 Further advice on demolition can be found in BS 6187.[17]

PRECAUTIONS FOR PARTICULAR SERVICES

99 This section gives advice on matters which relate to the main types of underground service. **It is additional information and should be read and used in conjunction with the advice contained in the 'Safe systems of work' section.**

Electricity cables

Planning the work and plans

100 Most service cables belong to the regional electricity company (look under 'Electricity' in the telephone directory). However, it is possible that some cables belong to other bodies such as the highway or roads authority, the street lighting authority, electricity generating companies, National Grid Company, Ministry of Defence, railway operator (usually Railtrack) or other companies.

101 Risk assessment should take into account the nature of local electrical hazards, such as the presence of a solid, fringe-fused cable system, as exists, for example, in London.

102 Figure 7 shows an example of an electricity cable plan. Note, however, that symbols vary between utilities and advice should be sought from the issuing office. Remember that high-voltage cables may be shown on separate plans from low-voltage cables.

103 For electricity cables more than other services, there may be a need to make dead for the work to proceed safely. It should be remembered that normally electricity companies have to give five days notice to customers whose supply is to be disconnected (see footnote to paragraph 32) and so, combined with other logistics of the process, making dead will normally take longer than five days.

Cable locating devices

104 Hum detectors are simple to use but they do not detect all cables - see paragraph 61. A locator with a radio frequency detection mode may detect cables which a hum detector may miss and should be used as a back-up check.

105 If a cable recorded on a plan cannot be located, seek appropriate assistance or advice. If digging has to start before such assistance or advice has been obtained, extreme care should be taken.

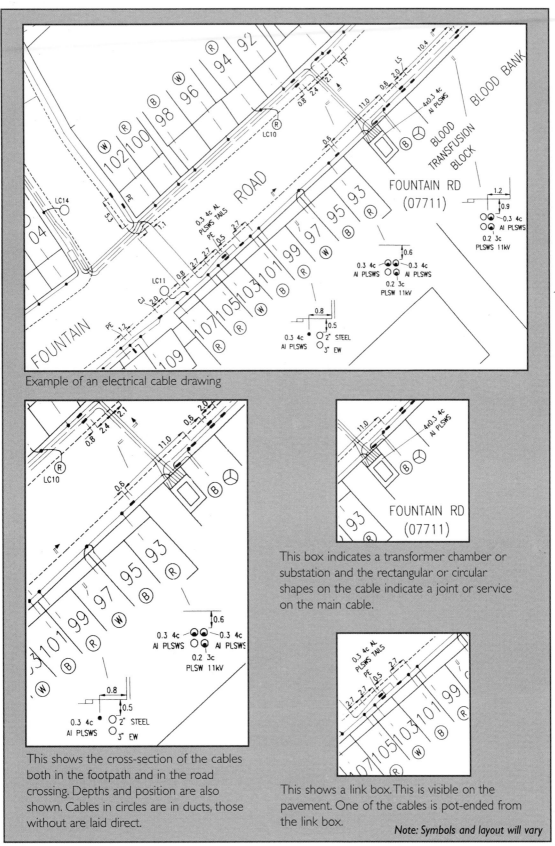

Example of an electrical cable drawing

This box indicates a transformer chamber or substation and the rectangular or circular shapes on the cable indicate a joint or service on the main cable.

This shows the cross-section of the cables both in the footpath and in the road crossing. Depths and position are also shown. Cables in circles are in ducts, those without are laid direct.

This shows a link box. This is visible on the pavement. One of the cables is pot-ended from the link box.

Note: Symbols and layout will vary

Figure 7   Example of an electricity plan

Safe digging practice

106 In most cases there will be no permanent surface marker posts or other visible indication of the presence of a buried cable. Even if no cables are shown on plans or detected by a locator, there may still be cables present, which could be live and a close watch should be kept for any signs which could indicate their presence.

107 Most underground cables are laid in trenches between 450 mm and 1 m deep. Some high-voltage (HV) cables will be deeper. However **depths should never be assumed.** Cables can be found just below the surface and even shallow excavations (for example for removal of a footpath base course) may be a source of danger. Remember this, particularly where:

■ the ground has been disturbed; or

■ lifting paving slabs or kerb stones; or

■ there are cellars or structures such as bridges in the area which may have prevented cables being laid at standard depths.

108 Cables may have been laid directly in the ground with a bed or surround of fine soil or sand, or in cement-bound sand, or in earthenware or plastic pipes or ducts. Very occasionally they may be in steel pipes. They may have a layer of tiles, slabs or coloured plastic marker tape laid above them. On the railway infrastructure, yellow plastic mesh is often used to cover them. However, any such protection may have been disturbed and moved and should not be relied upon to give an accurate indication of a cable position. Although most HV cables would normally have tiles or marker tapes laid over them, low-voltage (LV) cables and some HV cables, where they have been installed in ducts as 'trenchless' installations, may be laid without separate protective cover.

109 A cable is positively located only when it has been safely exposed. Even then, digging should still proceed with care as there may be other cables and services adjacent or lower down. In addition, some lines of 11 kV or greater can be laid out as separate single phase cables, spread out up to 600 mm across, particularly near cable joints.

110 Occasionally, cables are terminated in the ground by means of a seal, sometimes with external mechanical protection. These 'pot-ended' or 'bottle-ended' cables should be treated as live and should not be assumed to be abandoned or disused. They can be difficult to detect with locators even when 'live'.

111 Sometimes there may also be joints in cables. These may be enclosed in earthenware pipes, filled compound, or be of cast iron or plastic epoxy-filled casings. They need proper support and should not be roughly treated. They should not be moved except in consultation with the owner.

112 Using hand-held power tools to break up hard surfaces often leads to accidents. Where practicable, such power tools should only be used 500 mm or more away from the indicated line of a cable buried in or below a hard surface. Having done so, the cable should then be positively located by careful hand digging under the hard surface. The hard surface should be gradually removed until the cable is exposed. If the cable is not so exposed then it must be assumed to be embedded within the surface. Where possible a cable locator should be used as a depth guide down the side of the excavation. The 500 mm safety margin may be reduced:

■ where congestion of buried cables renders it impracticable; or

■ where surface obstructions limit the space available;

but only if the line of the cable has been positively identified by plans and confirmed by a locator.

113 Because of the difficulty in confirming depth, hand-held power tools should never be used over the cable unless either:

■ the cable has already been exposed by digging under the surface to be broken out and it is at a safe depth (at least 300 mm) below the bottom of the hard surface material; or

■ physical precautions have been taken to prevent the tool striking the cable.

Cables in concrete

114 Excavating close to electricity cables buried in concrete is dangerous. For this reason alone electricity cables should not be buried in concrete and the owners should ensure that their own employees and contractors are aware that this practice is unacceptable.

115 Using mechanical means to break up concrete can cause damage to cables and if the cable is live, anyone present is likely to be injured.

116 Careful planning is important to find alternative routes or, failing that, to arrange for the cable to be made dead (see also paragraph 103 and the footnote to paragraph 32). Cable owners are likely to want to attend the site to verify the circumstances surrounding any request to make dead. Electricity companies should co-operate, subject to the request being reasonable, and deal with the request as soon as possible. An alternative supply or bypass arrangement could be used to help allow the cable to be made dead.

117 **Work with the cable live should only be done if it is unreasonable in all the circumstances for the cable to be dead and suitable precautions are taken to prevent injury.** If there is no alternative route, and the cable cannot be made dead, then alternative safe methods of excavation should be agreed with the cable owners. Remember that powered hand tools used close to live cables are likely to represent the greatest risk of injury.

118 When excavation can proceed safely only after a buried cable has been made dead, and where permits-to-work or other safety documents are used, the parties involved should continue to liaise to ensure that work covered by the permit is completed, and workmen are clear, before the circuit is re-energised. Where it is clear there is a risk of damage to a cable during the course of any work, the owner may wish to have a presence on site.

119 Where mechanical excavators are used in the possible vicinity of underground cables, the work should be arranged so that damage to cables is avoided so far as is reasonably practicable and so that everyone is kept well clear of the excavator bucket while it is digging. Drivers should have been instructed to stay in the cab if a cable is struck. If they have to leave the cab, they should jump clear. If drivers climb down, they may be electrocuted. When a cable is struck, a watch should be kept on the machine and no one should go down into the excavation or approach the mechanical excavator or the cable until the cable owner has made the damaged cable safe.

120 With electricity cable accidents, there may be flash burns, spatter burns from molten metal and electrical burns. Direct electric shock is rare. Where electricity cables may be encountered during excavation work, employers should consider in their risk assessments whether the work justifies wearing clothing designed to protect against electric arc, or flame-retardant clothing. Advice on the suitability and performance of personal protective clothing should be available from reputable companies specialising in its supply.

121 Where cables have been exposed:

- any damage should be reported to the cable owners immediately and work should not be undertaken in the vicinity of a damaged cable until the owner has investigated its condition;

- for more than 1 m and they cross a trench, support should be provided. Where advice and help is needed to do this, the cable owner should be contacted. If the exposed cable length is shorter than 1 m, support should still be considered if joints have been exposed or the cable appears otherwise vulnerable to damage;

■ suitable precautions should be taken to prevent damage from ongoing work in the excavation. This may involve for example the use of physical means (eg timber boards, sandbags etc) to prevent mechanical damage. Materials or equipment which could damage or penetrate the outer sheath of the cable should not be used. Cables lying in the bottom of an excavation are particularly vulnerable and should be protected by nail-free wooden planks, troughing or other suitable means;

■ cables should not be moved aside unless the operation is supervised by the cable owners;

■ precautions should be taken to prevent access by members of the public, especially children.

Gas pipes

122 Most underground gas pipes are operated by either BG Transco or other public gas transporters (PGT) (look under 'Gas' in the telephone directory). The main exception is estates fed from bulk-stored liquefied petroleum gas (LPG) where the pipes may be owned by the estate owners or other private individuals. In the latter case, owners/managers should be able to provide information, but on certain estates (for example caravans or other rented accommodation) owners and managers may not be available round the clock. Further information may also be obtained from the LPG supplier whose name and telephone number (manned 24 hours) should be displayed at the bulk storage vessel compound, or, for buried LPG tanks, at the segregated area above the tanks. The risk from leaking LPG is greater than from a natural gas leak as it is heavier than air and does not disperse so readily. It can also travel great distances below ground level before accumulating at low level.

Planning the work

123 It is important that the location of underground gas pipelines is considered when planning building, excavation, landfill or other such work. Such activities may either cause damage to the pipelines or deny access to them for maintenance purposes. Early contact at the planning stage is very important as it will allow full discussion of proposals to ensure the safety of plant and operators.

124 Where heavy plant may have to cross the line of a gas pipe during construction work, the number of crossing points should be kept to a minimum. They should be clearly indicated and crossings not allowed at other places along the line of the pipe. Where the pipe is not adequately protected by an existing road, crossing points should be suitably reinforced with sleepers, steel plates or a specially constructed reinforced concrete raft as necessary. The PGT will advise on the type of reinforcement necessary.

Plans

125 Plans do not normally show the position of service connections and their existence should be assumed. It may be possible to estimate the probable line of the service connection pipe from the gas meter position, or from the point of entry into the premises.

126 Gas plant may also be shown by PGT valve boxes, pits and housings. However, covers for valve boxes and pits will sometimes not show clearly whether gas is the service present; if in doubt, contact the PGT. Pits and housings may also indicate the presence of small-bore control pipes.

127 Where the presence of gas pipes which operate at pressures of 2 bar (30 psig) and above is indicated, consult the PGT before work begins.

128 An example of a plan of underground gas pipes is shown in Figure 8.

Pipe-locating devices

129 Radio frequency detection or transmitter/receiver types of locating device should be used to help locate metallic gas pipes before excavation. However, many gas pipes are made of polyethylene (PE) and unless they incorporate a tracer wire, these cannot be traced by such devices. As a result it is especially important to use plans and safe digging practices.

Safe digging practice and avoidance of long-term damage

130 The depth of cover for gas mains laid in a roadway is normally about 750 mm, and for those laid in a footway about 600 mm. The depth of cover for gas service connections is normally about 450 mm in both roads and footways. However, on private property, including at entry positions to buildings, the depth of cover for the service connection may be less, about 375 mm. High-pressure gas transmission pipelines are usually buried with at least 900 mm cover. Remember that these depths **are only a guide**, and that pipes may be found at shallower depths.

131 Gas pipes are generally laid directly in the ground, although in certain soils selective backfill may have been used as a bed and pipe surround and on occasion pipes may be laid in ducts. Ductile iron pipe will sometimes be found wrapped in loose-fit polyethylene (PE) sleeving as protection against corrosion. PE mains may be inserted into redundant iron gas mains and PE service connection pipes may be inserted into yellow convoluted ducting on new housing estates.

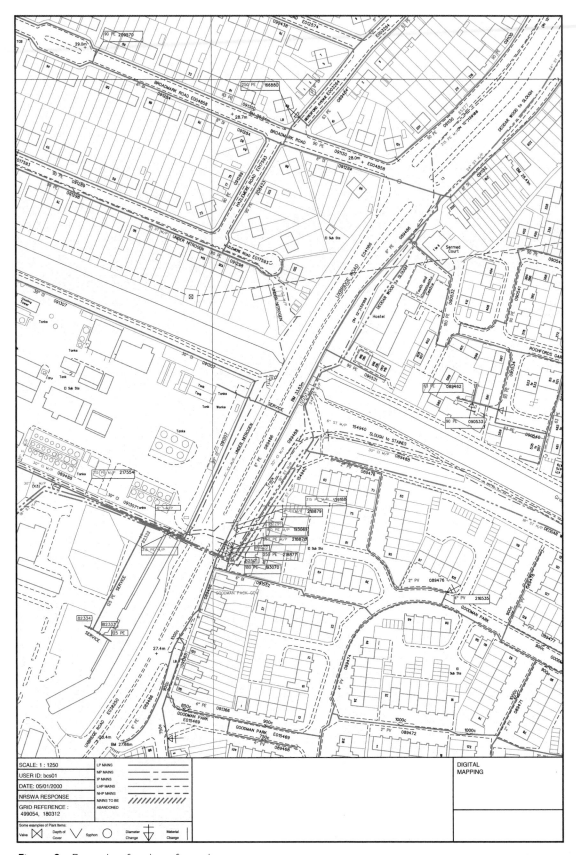

Figure 8   Example of a plan of gas pipes

132 Markers may also have been used to indicate gas services, namely:

- marker tiles, which may have been used above gas pipes, for example when they have been laid at shallow depths in bridges or above cellars;

- coloured plastic markers, including for PE mains (see Figure 9);

- marker posts/plates, which may show the position and size of valves or test points on gas mains.

  However, such markers may have been disturbed and should not be relied upon as an accurate indicator of position.

133 PE gas pipes should be located by hand digging before mechanical excavation begins. This may also be necessary for metallic pipes if they have not been successfully located by a pipe-locating device. This is particularly

Figure 9 Yellow plastic tape, laid above a gas pipe

important for service connection pipes which will not be marked on plans. A suitable hand digging method is to dig a trial trench along the road near the kerb or in the footway where the service connection pipes are likely to be at their shallowest. When the positions and depth of the pipes have been determined, work can proceed.

134 Gas pipes may have projections such as valve housings, siphons and stand pipes which are not shown on the plans. To allow for this, mechanical excavators should not be used within 500 mm of a gas pipe. Greater safety distances may be advised by the PGT or operator, depending on pressure.

135 The danger created by damaging a gas pipe with an excavator is much greater than if the damage is done with a hand-held power tool (the opposite is true for work near electricity cables and this is reflected in the different safe digging practices). It is worth remembering that the effects may not only occur at the point of impact, for example:

■ damage to a service connection may result in unseen damage to the connection inside the building;

■ gas from a damaged pipe may travel along the line of a service pipe into a building, causing a dangerous build-up of gas there.

136 Hand-held power tools can also damage buried gas pipes and should be used with care until the exact position of a buried pipe has been determined. They may be used to break a paved or concrete surface above a gas pipe, unless there are any indications that the pipe is particularly shallow or close to the surface to be broken up.

137 Where pipe restraints or thrust blocks are close to gas mains, these (and the ground supporting them) should never be disturbed, as this can cause sudden failure of the main.

138 Because of the risks they pose, the following should not be undertaken without consultation with the PGT:

■ the use of explosives within 30 m of any gas pipe;

■ piling or vertical boring within 15 m of any gas pipe;

■ excavation work within 10 m of any above-ground gas installation;

■ building a manhole, chamber or other structure over, around or under a gas pipe;

■ work which results in a reduction of cover or protection over a pipe.

139 If welding or other hot work involving naked flames is to be carried out within 10 m of exposed gas plant, the PGT should be asked to check the atmosphere before work begins and monitoring should continue during the work. Care should be taken to ensure that no damage occurs, particularly to plastic gas pipes or to the protective coatings on other gas pipes.

140 If a gas leak is suspected, repairs should not be attempted. Instead the following action should be taken immediately:

- evacuate everyone from the immediate vicinity of the escape. If the service connection to a building or the adjacent main has been damaged, warn the occupants to leave the building, and any adjoining building, until it is safe for them to return;

- inform BG Transco by telephoning the gas emergency number 0800 111999. BG Transco will inform other PGTs if necessary;

- prohibit smoking, and extinguish all naked flames and other sources of ignition, within **at least 5 m** of the leak; and

- help PGT staff, police or fire services as requested.

141 It is important to report any damage, however slight, to the owner. Where an excavation uncovers a gas pipe with a damaged wrapping, the owner should be told so that repairs can be made to prevent future corrosion and leakage.

142 Where gas pipes cross or run alongside excavations, changes in backfill etc may cause differential ground settlement and increased stress in the pipe. For pipes alongside excavations, the degree of risk depends upon the depth of the excavation, the distance of the pipe from the excavation and the type of soil. Wherever an excavation may affect support for a gas pipe, the owner should be consulted. In some cases it may be necessary to divert the gas pipe before work begins. Further information is contained in the *Model consultative procedure for pipeline construction involving deep excavation.*[18]

143 When backfilling an exposed gas pipe, the following should be observed:

- backfill material adjacent to gas plant should be suitable fine material or sand, containing no stones, bricks or lumps of concrete;

- the backfill should be suitably compacted. Where the excavation has exposed an existing gas pipe, compaction should give comparable support and protection to that before the excavation. In all situations, compaction beneath the pipe is particularly important to prevent any settlement which would subsequently damage the pipe;

- there should be no power compaction until 200 mm cover of selected fine fill has been suitably compacted;

- concrete backfill should not be used within 300 mm of a gas pipe.

144 If road construction is close to the top of a gas pipe, the owner/operator should be asked about necessary precautions. The road construction depth should not be reduced without permission from the local highway or roads authority.

145 Anyone who carries out work near underground gas plant should observe any specific requirements made by PGT staff, and ensure that access to the plant by those staff is available at all times. No unauthorised repairs to gas pipes should be made. **If in doubt, seek advice from BG Transco or the other appropriate PGT, if different. The addresses and telephone numbers for all emergencies and enquiries can be found in the telephone directory under 'Gas'.**

Water pipes and sewers

146 To avoid the effects of frost, water mains and sewers are generally laid at depths of 900 mm or more; water services to premises are normally at about 750 mm cover, unless local circumstances necessitate shallower depths. In general, work near underground water pipes is of low risk and most precautions are more concerned with reducing the cost of damage than with eliminating hazard. However, there are some dangers, and precautions should include:

■ where work is carried out near water mains, plans should be obtained from the relevant water company and a pipe locator used. However, plastic pipes will not be detectable by most locating devices. Safe digging practices should be followed, using hand tools as far as is practicable;

■ at bends in mains, concrete thrust blocks may be used. Under no circumstances should either thrust blocks or the ground supporting them be disturbed, as this can cause sudden failure of the main;

■ exposed water pipes should be supported as necessary and the correct method of backfilling used. For advice, contact the relevant water company or water authority;

■ if a water pipe or its wrapping is damaged, the relevant water company or water authority and the owners of any other underground services which may be affected should be informed immediately. Unauthorised repairs should not be made.

Other pipelines

147 Other pipelines are used to convey a wide range of fluids including oils and other petrochemicals, ethylene, oxygen, nitrogen and similar industrial gases and a number of other chemicals.

148 The more hazardous of these pipelines (known as major accident hazard pipelines) will not normally be found in residential areas. They are usually in rural areas and often near chemical and petrochemical installations. Cross-country pipelines are also found in agricultural land. They usually cross roads, railways and motorways etc at right angles.

Planning the work and plans

149 It is important to consider the location of underground pipelines before carrying out building, excavation, landfill, or other such work. Such activities may not only cause damage to pipelines but could also affect access to them for maintenance purposes in the future.

150 Signs indicating the presence of buried pipelines should be looked for, for example marker posts often show where pipelines cross roads and other boundaries. Both the landowner and local authority should be contacted for further information; it is a statutory requirement for plans of pipelines to be lodged with local authorities.

151 Liaison with the pipeline operator is important, as information can be provided about not only the location but also the nature of the fluid being transported, any restrictions on excavations in the vicinity of the pipeline, the precautions to be taken during excavating and action to be taken in an emergency. Accordingly, where work is proposed near pipelines, the specific requirements of pipeline operators should be adhered to.

Pipe locators

152 The majority of these pipelines are of welded steel construction and locators of the radio frequency detection or the transmitter/receiver types can be used to locate them before excavation.

Safe digging practice

153 These pipelines may be laid directly in the ground, although sometimes selective backfill will have been used as a bed and pipe surround. They are normally buried with at least 900 mm cover and may be even deeper where they cross roads and railways. Therefore they are unlikely to be affected by shallow excavations.

154 Although marker posts/plates are sometimes used to indicate the position, size and ownership of pipelines, such markers may have been disturbed and should not be relied upon as an accurate indicator of position.

155 Pipelines should be located by hand digging before mechanical excavators are used nearby. In any event, mechanical excavators should not be used within 500 mm of a pipeline.

156 Most pipelines will be protected against corrosion by a coating. This will normally be:

- coal tar or bitumen - coloured black sometimes with traces of white limewash;

- polyethylene cladding - usually yellow; or

- fusion-bonded epoxy powder - can be any colour - usually green or beige.

157 Some pipelines will be protected against corrosion by an alternative method known as cathodic protection, which will be linked to the pipeline by cabling. Both pipeline coatings and cathodic protection systems are susceptible to damage, even with hand tools, so great care is needed when excavating and backfilling and physical means of prevention (such as boards etc) should be used where appropriate. It is important to report to the owner/operator any damage, including to the corrosion protection, before the service is reburied.

Telecommunication cables

158 Owners of the cables should be consulted on precautions, to avoid costly damage. No special precautions are required to prevent danger.

FIRST AID

159 Workers should know how to give emergency aid until help arrives. Competence in cardiopulmonary resuscitation and the immediate care of burns and unconsciousness would be an advantage. Help should be sought quickly if there is a serious accident and in remote locations means such as mobile phones, two-way radios etc may be the only way of doing this.

160 A casualty should not be moved unless in a position of danger. This is particularly important when the person has been thrown some distance and may have suffered injuries other than burns. People giving first aid should take care not to touch any exposed cables or tools that may be live.

161 Electric shock may cause unconsciousness, and the heart and breathing may stop; urgent action is then needed. It is essential to establish a clear airway and cardiopulmonary resuscitation should be given as soon as possible by someone competent and trained to do so.

162 Electrical burns are deceptive, with underlying damage possibly far more serious than appears on the surface. A sterile covering should be placed over the affected areas as soon as possible to reduce the risk of infection, and all burns cases should receive professional medical attention. Urgent help is essential for severe burns, which can prove fatal, and all cases of injury resulting from an electrical accident should be referred for professional treatment.

163 A first-aid container or small travelling first-aid kit should be provided with the standard contents as described in *First aid at work*.[19] There should be enough provided for the number of employees involved. Sterile triangular bandages and sterile dressings can be used to cover burns and a sterile, individually wrapped, paper disposable sheet or similar sterile

covering may be used for burns involving an extensive body area.

164 Advice on appropriate sources of first aid-training can be obtained from local offices of the Employment Medical Advisory Service.

APPENDIX I LEGISLATION

1   The following summary outlines the main legal requirements which apply to work near buried services. The list is not exhaustive and does not give a definitive interpretation of the law. It summarises the main issues to bear in mind when carrying out such work.

The Health and Safety at Work etc Act 1974

2   The 1974 Act applies to all work activities whether or not the Construction (Health, Safety and Welfare) Regulations 1996[20] or the Construction (Design and Management) Regulations 1994[3] apply.

3   Section 2(1) imposes a duty on an employer to ensure so far as is reasonably practicable the health, safety and welfare of employees while at work. This extends to the provision and maintenance of safe systems of work as well as such information, instruction, training and supervision as is necessary.

4   Section 3(1) imposes a duty on employers to take precautions, so far as is reasonably practicable, to ensure the health and safety of people not in their employment. This duty could apply to any owner/operator of underground services, to clients, local authorities or other utilities or contractors who have the necessary records and other information required by other contractors or subcontractors. Section 3(2) imposes a similar duty on the self-employed for the health and safety of themselves and others.

5   Section 4(2) imposes a duty on people in control of non-domestic premises to ensure, so far as is reasonably practicable, the health and safety of people not in their employment who are using those premises. The definition of premises is wide-ranging and is not confined to buildings.

6   Section 7 imposes duties on each employee to take reasonable care for their own health and safety and for the health and safety of anyone else who may be affected by their acts or omissions at work, and to co-operate with their employer to enable the employer to comply with their duties.

The Management of Health and Safety at Work Regulations 1999

7   These Regulations require employers and the self-employed to assess the risks arising from work activities.[5] They should do this with a view to identifying the measures which need to be taken to comply with relevant health and safety legislation, therefore eliminating risks where possible and controlling those which remain.

The Construction (Design and Management) Regulations 1994

8   The Construction (Design and Management) Regulations 1994 apply to many construction projects (application is defined in regulation 3) and set out requirements in relation to their

design and management. They place responsibilities on all those who can contribute to improving health and safety including clients, designers and contractors. Risks should be properly managed by action during the design, planning and execution phases of the project.

The Construction (Health, Safety and Welfare) Regulations 1996

9   These Regulations apply to construction work as defined by regulation 2(1) of the Regulations. They therefore cover most work in the vicinity of buried services. In particular, regulation 12(8) requires, where reasonably practicable, the identification of underground cables and services before work starts and positive action to prevent injury.

The Provision and Use of Work Equipment Regulations 1998

10   These Regulations require that equipment is maintained in good repair. Employers should ensure that employees who use work equipment or who manage or supervise its use, have received adequate training in the risks involved, methods of use and precautions to be adopted.

The Electricity at Work Regulations 1989

11   The Regulations require that those in control of part or all of an electrical system should ensure that the system is safe when provided, safe to use, and that it is maintained in a safe condition.[21] They also require that any work activity on or near an electrical system be carried out in such a manner as to prevent danger - excavation work should not be carried out unless all suitable and sufficient steps have been taken to identify and, as far as is reasonably practicable, prevent any risk from any underground cable or other underground electrical service (regulation 4(3)). Regulation 14 requires that work should not be done on or near a live conductor, where danger may arise, unless:

- it is unreasonable in all the circumstances for it to be dead; and

- it is reasonable in all the circumstances for the work to be done while it is live; and

- suitable precautions are taken to prevent injury.

The Reporting of Injuries, Diseases and Dangerous Occurrences Regulations 1995

12   These Regulations require employers and the self-employed to report certain occupational injuries, diseases and dangerous occurrences[22,23] to

the relevant enforcing authority (for incidents arising during excavation work this will almost certainly be the local office of the Health and Safety Executive).

13   Any injury which results in a worker being unable to carry out the full range of their duties for more than three days (including rest days and holidays) is reportable. There is also a range of injuries defined as major injuries. These include injuries from electric shock or electrical burns (including those from arcing), causing unconsciousness or requiring resuscitation or leading to hospitalisation for more than 24 hours.

14   Where there are no reportable injuries, underground electrical cable strikes become reportable as dangerous occurrences where the resulting fire or electrical explosion had the potential to cause death or if it puts the cable out of action for more than 24 hours.

15   Certain pipeline incidents, including gas escapes, are also reportable as dangerous occurrences by the operator of the pipeline. Schedule 2, part 1, paragraph 14 lists dangerous occurrences associated with pipelines which are reportable. (Certain pipelines are exempted, corresponding to those to which the Pipelines Safety Regulations do NOT apply, eg water mains, drains and sewers.) The dangerous occurrences include:

■   the uncontrolled or accidental escape of anything from, or inrush of anything into, a pipeline which has the potential to cause the death of, major injury or damage to the health of any person or which results in the pipeline being shut down for more than 24 hours;

■   any damage to any part of a pipeline which has the potential to cause the death of, major injury or damage to the health of any person or which results in the pipeline being shut down for more than 24 hours;

■   any substantial and unintentional change in the position of a pipeline requiring immediate attention to safeguard the integrity or safety of a pipeline.

The Gas Safety (Management) Regulations 1996

16   These Regulations are aimed at ensuring the natural gas distribution network is safely managed.[24] To deal with gas leaks, they require the following:

■   BG Group plc (or its successors) to provide a continuously manned, national freephone telephone service, so that people can report gas escapes;

■   where BG Group plc (or its successors) is notified of escapes they should straight away notify the relevant gas conveyor or emergency service provider;

■   the relevant gas conveyor or emergency service provider should go to where the gas is escaping as soon as reasonably practicable;

■   gas conveyors/emergency service providers should stop gas escaping within 12 hours.

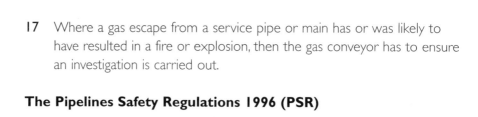

17   Where a gas escape from a service pipe or main has or was likely to have resulted in a fire or explosion, then the gas conveyor has to ensure an investigation is carried out.

The Pipelines Safety Regulations 1996 (PSR)

18   These Regulations deal with the safe design, construction and operation of pipelines. The scope includes requirements that:

■   no person shall cause such damage to a pipeline as may give rise to a danger; and

■   pipeline operators shall take reasonable steps to inform people of the existence and whereabouts of a pipeline to prevent damage to it.

19   The Approved Code of Practice L81 *Design, construction and installation of gas service pipes*[25] gives practical guidance with the application of PSR with specific regard to gas service pipes. It requires gas service pipes to be installed in such a way that they are least likely to be affected by third party interference or subject to accidental damage.

Other legislation

Gas Act 1995*

20   The Act updates provisions in the Gas Act 1986, including new licensing arrangements for public gas transporters, permitting competition in the domestic gas market.

New Roads and Street Works Act 1991 (NRSWA)†

21   This Act requires utilities and other undertakers (undertaker is a defined term under the Act) to give notice of their planned works under a variety of circumstances, depending upon the type of street in which the works are to be carried out and the type of works to be done. Emergency, urgent and some minor works can be started without issuing notice.

22   The Act also requires undertakers to record the location of apparatus belonging to them, to keep records up to date and to make them available for inspection at all reasonable hours, free of charge to any person having authority to carry out works in the street.

---

* Enforced by the DTI.
† Enforced by highway or roads authorities.

23 The terms 'emergency', 'urgent' and 'minor' works referred to above relate only to notifications for the purpose of the NRSWA and do not affect the legal obligations under the Health and Safety at Work Act (HSW Act) to give and obtain information needed to ensure safe working. While procedures under NRSWA may provide information needed under the HSW Act, owners of buried services will also need arrangements for providing such information in other cases, such as for 'emergency' works, to comply with HSW Act duties. HSW Act requirements apply to all work regardless of NRSWA classification and include work not covered by the NRSWA. There is also a specific duty on electricity companies to supply information under the Electricity Supply Regulations (see paragraph 25 below).

24 Section 67 of NRSWA requires that for any street works, work is supervised by a person qualified under the Street Works (Qualifications of Supervisors and Operatives) Regulations 1992. There also has to be an operative qualified under the same Regulations on site while work is in progress. These qualifications are certificates of competence issued by an Approved Body or an equivalent qualification issued in another EU state.

Electricity Supply Regulations 1988*

25 A supplier of electricity has a duty under Regulation 36 of the Regulations to make and, so far as is reasonably practicable, keep up to date 'a map or series of maps indicating the position and depth below surface level of all his works'. The supplier must provide these maps free of charge to anyone who has good reason for requiring them. Regulation 10 of the 1988 Regulations imposes requirements for the protection of underground cables and regulation 11 imposes requirements for the depth and manner of their installation.

Fire Services Act 1947

26 Section 16[†] requires notice to be given to the fire authority of works which will affect a water supply or a fire hydrant.

---

* Enforced by the DTI.
† Enforced by fire authorities.

APPENDIX 2 SUGGESTED TEXT FOR WORKERS' INFORMATION

Anyone who works near underground services should be properly trained in safe procedures. Information issued to employees can usefully supplement this training and act as a reminder of the main points. A suggested text is given below. It could be usefully adapted to meet the needs of individual organisations by adding supervisors' names, contact points etc.

Advice to site personnel when working near underground services

- Underground services, particularly electricity and gas, can be dangerous. Damage to electricity cables can cause a flash, leading to severe burns or even death. Gas leaks can cause fire or explosion.

- Damage can result from excavation or penetration of the ground, for example by a road pin.

- Underground services may be found in roads, footpaths and on sites. Always assume that they are present. Treat all services as LIVE, despite their apparent physical condition.

- Accidents have happened because people have mistaken one service for another, for example black plastic-covered electricity cables look like black plastic water pipes and cast iron gas and water mains look alike. Check before you act.

Before starting work:

- Make sure you have plans of the underground services in the area. This may not always be possible for emergency works. Remember that service connection cables and pipes from the main to a building or street light may not be shown.

- Use a cable- and pipe-locator to trace electricity cables and metal pipes. You should have been trained how to do this. If in doubt, or if you have any difficulty, ask your supervisor for advice.

- Mark the positions of the cables and pipes using paint or other waterproof marking on the ground.

- Look for signs of service connection cables or pipes, for example a gas meter or service connection entry into a house or a street light.

- Hand dig trial holes (as many as necessary) to confirm the position of services in the area of your work. This is particularly important if there are plastic pipes, which cannot be found using a locator.

When you start work:

- Wherever possible, hand dig near buried services. Spades and shovels are safer than picks, pins or forks.

- Check that any cable which is embedded in concrete and has to be broken out has been made dead before work starts, or that another safe way of working has been agreed with the cable owner (often the regional electricity company).

- Watch out for signs of services as work continues. Repeat checks with the cable- and pipe-locator as the excavation progresses.

- Backfill around services with a fine material. Do NOT use flints, bricks, mass concrete or similar material.

- Report any damage to a cable, pipe or pipe coating. Even if there is no immediate danger, damage could cause danger at a later date. Do not attempt repairs.

- Do not use hand-held power tools within 500 mm of the marked position of an electricity cable (if the number of services present or surface obstructions makes this impossible seek further advice).

- Do not use hand-held power tools directly over the marked line of a cable unless:
  - you have already found the cable at that position by careful hand digging beneath the surface and it is at a safe depth (at least 300 mm) below the bottom of the surface to be broken; or
  - physical means have been used to prevent the tool striking it.

- Do not use a mechanical excavator within 500 mm of a gas pipe. If an excavator is used near an electricity cable keep everyone clear of the bucket while it is digging.

- Do not use exposed services as a convenient step or handhold.

- Do not handle or attempt to alter the position of an exposed service.

- Do not install plant close to an existing service. Ask your supervisor to tell you what the separation should be.

- Do not build existing services into a manhole or other structure or encase them in concrete.

If you suspect a gas leak:

■ Evacuate everyone from the immediate area of the escape. Remember that if a service connection to a building has been damaged, it may cause a leak in the building. Warn the occupants of the building, and of adjoining buildings, to leave.

■ Do not attempt repairs.

■ Telephone BG Transco on 0800 111999 immediately.

■ Ban smoking, naked flames and other sources of ignition within at least 5 m of the leak.

■ Help Transco, the Police or Fire Services as requested.

REMEMBER - IF IN DOUBT, ASK.

REFERENCES

1   *Safety at street works and road works. A Code of Practice issued by the Secretaries of State for Transport, Scotland and Wales under sections 65 and 124 of the New Roads and Street Works Act 1991* The Stationery Office 1992 ISBN 0 11 551144 X

2   *Health and safety in excavations* HSG185 HSE Books 1999 ISBN 0 7176 1563 4

3   *Managing construction for health and safety. Construction (Design and Management) Regulations 1994. Approved Code of Practice* L54 HSE Books 1995 ISBN 0 7176 0792 5

4   *A guide to managing health and safety in construction* HSE Books 1995 ISBN 0 7176 0755 0

5   *Management of health and safety at work. Management of Health and Safety at Work Regulations 1999. Approved Code of Practice* L21 HSE Books 2000 ISBN 0 7176 2488 9 (Due to be published in March 2000)

6   *A guide to the Pipelines Safety Regulations 1996. Guidance on Regulations* L82 HSE Books 1996 ISBN 0 7176 1182 5

7   *Designing for health and safety in construction* HSE Books 1995 ISBN 0 7176 0807 7

8   *Recommendations for the exchange of records of apparatus between utilities* NJUG 9 National Joint Utilities Group 1994

9   *Recommendations for dealing with reported gas escapes* IGE/SR/20 Institution of Gas Engineers 1992

10   *The identification of small buried mains and services* NJUG 4 National Joint Utilities Group 1995

11   *Specification for identification of pipelines and services* British Standard BS 1710: 1984 (1991)

12   *New Roads and Street Works Act 1991. Specification for the reinstatement of openings in highways. A Code of Practice approved by the Secretaries of State for Transport, Wales and Scotland under sections 71 and 130 of the Act* The Stationery Office 1992 ISBN 0 11 551143 1

13   *Trenchless methods of construction* Technical Note 127, available from Customer Services, Construction Industry Research and Information Association (CIRIA), 6 Storeys Gate, London SW1 3AU, Tel: 0171 222 8891

14   *Horizontal directional drilling and impact moling* IGE/SR/26 Institution of Gas Engineers 1999

15   *Recommended positioning of utilities' mains and plant for new works* NJUG 7 National Joint Utilities Group 1997

16 *Electrical safety on construction sites* HSG141 HSE Books 1995 ISBN 0 7176 1000 4

17 *Code of Practice for demolition* British Standard BS 6187: 1982

18 *Model consultative procedure for pipeline construction involving deep excavation* M060/ERS 1993 Water UK and BG Group plc, available from BG Technology Ltd, Gas Research and Technology Centre, Ashby Road, Loughborough LE11 3GR, Tel: 01509 282525

19 *First aid at work; Health and safety (First-Aid) Regulations 1981. Approved Code of Practice and guidance* L74 HSE Books 1997 ISBN 0 7176 1050 0

20 *Construction (Health, Safety and Welfare) Regulations 1996* SI 1592/1996 The Stationery Office ISBN 0 11 035904 6

21 *Memorandum of Guidance on the Electricity at Work Regulations 1989. Guidance on Regulations* HSR25 HSE Books 1989 ISBN 0 7176 1602 9

22 *A Guide to the Reporting of Injuries, Diseases and Dangerous Occurrences Regulations 1995* L73 HSE Books 1999 ISBN 0 7176 2431 5

23 *RIDDOR explained. The Reporting of Injuries, Diseases and Dangerous Occurrences Regulations 1995* HSE31(rev1) HSE Books 1999

24 *A Guide to the Gas Safety (Management) Regulations 1996. Guidance on Regulations* L80 HSE Books 1996 ISBN 0 7176 1159 0

25 *Design, construction and installation of gas service pipes. The Pipelines Safety Regulations 1996. Approved Code of Practice and guidance* L81 HSE Books 1996 ISBN 0 7176 1172 8

For details of how to obtain HSE publications, see inside back cover.

British Standards are available from BSI Customer Services, 389 Chiswick High Road, London W4 4AL, Tel: 0181 996 7000 Fax: 0181 996 7001.

The Stationery Office (formerly HMSO) publications are available from The Publications Centre, PO Box 276, London SW8 5DT, Tel: 0870 600 5522. They are also available from bookshops.

NJUG publications are available from NJUG, 30 Millbank, London SW1P 4RD, Tel: 0171 963 5720.

IGE publications are available from Institution of Gas Engineers, 21 Portland Place, London W1N 3AF, Tel: 0171 636 6603.

FURTHER INFORMATION

HSE guidance

The HSE video *Alive ... or Dead?* covering the hazards from buried electricity cables is available for sale or hire from HSE Videos, PO Box 35, Wetherby, West Yorks LS23 7EX, Tel: 0845 741 9411

Health and safety in construction HSG150 HSE Books 1996 ISBN 0 7176 1143 4

Construction Information Sheets:

Safety in excavations CIS8(rev1) HSE Books 1997

Construction (Design and Management) Regulations 1994: The role of the client CIS39
HSE Books 1995

Construction (Design and Management) Regulations 1994: The role of the planning supervisor CIS40
HSE Books 1995

Construction (Design and Management) Regulations 1994: The role of the designer CIS41
HSE Books 1995

Construction (Design and Management) Regulations 1994: The pre-tender stage health and safety plan CIS42 HSE Books 1995

Construction (Design and Management) Regulations 1994: The health and safety plan during the construction phase CIS43 HSE Books 1995

Construction (Design and Management) Regulations 1994: The health and safety file CIS44
HSE Books 1995

Printed and published by the Health and Safety Executive   C200   I/00